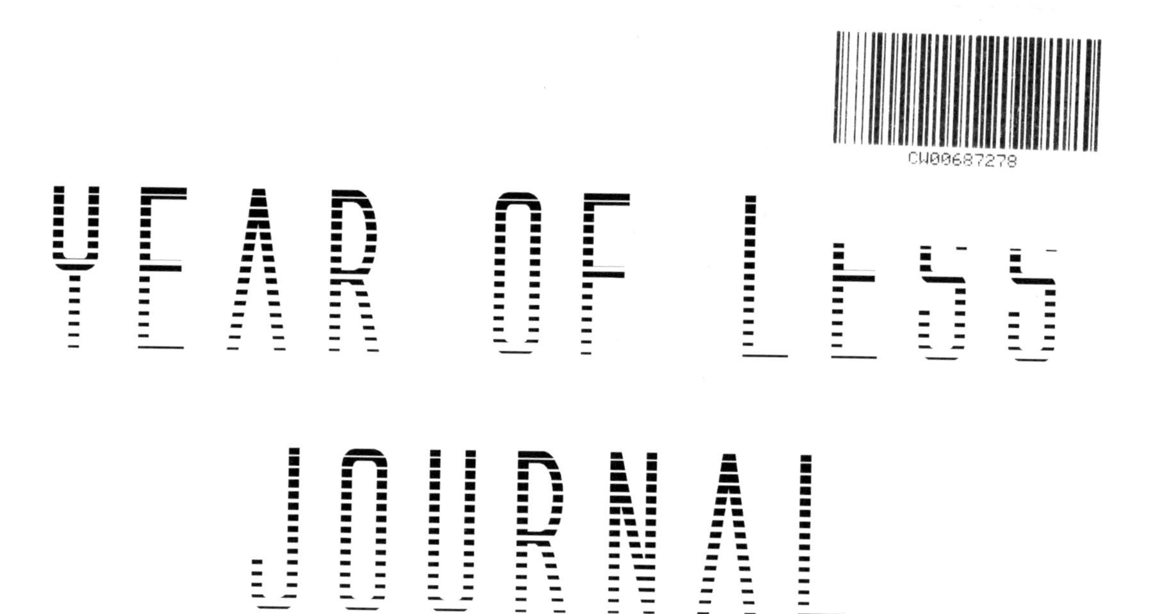

Letting go to make room for something better

By Valerie Morris

WELCOME

Welcome to a year of less! The reality is that while we are getting rid of so much from our lives, we ultimately will be filling it with so much more of the good stuff! Some months we will focus on physical things, some months digital things, and some months the theme is more mental and emotional.

HOW THIS WORKS:

You can go in order or jump around - focus on whatever theme works best for you and what you need each month. There are twelve things in this journal for each of the twelve months in the next year and we've found that a month is a good time frame to dive into one topic. Don't rush the process! Give yourself time to think through, dwell on, and make steps.

JOIN US ONLINE:

Do you want to share the journey with others who are walking through the same process? Want even more resources and tips on each month's theme? We have a growing group of regular people, just like you and me, who are on the journey to simplify life and make room for more of the good stuff!

Join us at our Facebook Group (www.facebook.com/groups/lifeofless/)

To The Journey!

Valerie

LESS CLUTTER MORE CLARITY

Ever feel like you're literally drowning by your STUFF? I find that I fill the space I have available, which can mean a lot of stuff if I'm not careful. Clutter can make me feel like life is more stressful than it really is. My personal mantra has always been like the quote below to focus on things I need and things I love. However, even knowing these things doesn't make me immune. It's easy for clutter to build up in our spaces. The more I am aware of clutter in my life, the more easily I can build systems and habits to reduce it.

- *"The most important things in life aren't things." - Anthony J. D'Angelo*
- *"Simplicity is making the journey of this life with just baggage enough." - Author Unknown*
- *"Your children need your presence, more than your presents." - Jesse Jackson*
- *"Have nothing in your houses that you do not know to be useful or believe to be beautiful." - William Morris*

Inventory:

What zones in my home are full of too much clutter?

____

____

Where does my clutter come from? Free stuff? Sales I can't pass up? Sentimental feelings? Other?

____

____

____

____

How does clutter make me feel? What kinds of emotions does it trigger?

____

____

____

____

Action Steps:

- Get rid of one thing a day for a week.
- Start a box of things to donate. Add a few items to it initially, but keep it handy to add items as you discover them in your day to day.
- Follow the one-in-one-out rule this week and look and see what you brought into your home that is new vs. how many things in your life you have let go of.

NOTES

LESS YES MORE NO

Are you a people pleaser? Are you a dreamer? Do you love meeting BIG dreams and goals? If you can resonate with any of those questions, odds are, you know the feeling when you have said yes to way to many things. You find yourself stretched too thin, and not able to give your very best to any of these things. Saying "no" is something we could all use a little bit more of in our lives - at least I know it's true for me. This one is hard because it can feel borderline icky or mean, but the truth is that we need to say "no" more often so that we can instead say "yes" to the things we really have a passion for. Anyone else with me?

- *"Tone is the hardest part of saying no." - Jonathan Price*
- *"If you want more time, freedom, and energy, start saying no." - Anonymous*
- *"Half of the troubles of this life can be traced to saying yes too quickly and not saying no soon enough." Josh Billings*
- *"Say no to everything, so you can say yes to the one thing." -Richie Norton*
- *"NO is a complete sentence. It does not require an explanation to follow. You can truly answer someone's request with a simple No." - Sharon E. Rainey*
- *"When you say 'yes' to others, make sure you're not saying 'no' to yourself." -Paulo Coelho*

Inventory:

What have I said "yes" to today?

____

____

____

This week?

____

____

____

This Month?

____

____

____

This Year?

____

____

____

Can I delegate or hire out for any of these items I listed above? If so, what and how?

____

____

Action Steps:

List out all of the things you have say "no" to in the last 24 hours.

____

____

____

____

____

____

Choose 2-3 things to commit to delegating out within the next two weeks.

____

____

____

Write out 2-3 scripts of ways to say no in a way that feels right for you. Practice saying them to yourself daily in front of your mirror, while you're driving in the car, or in the shower.

NOTES

LESS WORRY MORE FREEDOM

Folks, this is hard! I hold onto my worries so tightly, even though I know they don't bring me anything good. I've been living this worry-filled life for so long, it's hard to consider life without it. But, the few glimpses I've seen of a life filled with less worry, the more I have felt freedom and a feeling of lightness. It's time to stop feeling weighed down by worry and instead live today with all fullness possible!

- *"Worry does not empty tomorrow of its sorrow, it empties today of its strength."* - Corrie ten Boom
- *"Worry often gives a small thing a big shadow."* - Swedish Proverb
- *"My life has been full of terrible misfortunes most of which never happened."* - Michel de Montaigne
- *"Therefore do not be anxious about tomorrow, for tomorrow will be anxious for itself. Sufficient for the day is its own trouble." The Bible, Matthew 6:34*

Inventory:

Am I a natural worrywart, or do I tend to let things go?

____

____

What are the things that habitually keep me up at night? Are there any patterns I can find in these?

____

____

____

____

Think of a time when you worried about something so much that you could visibly see it affect your day and physically feel it affect your body. What was it and what actually happened in real life? Were your worries warranted?

____

____

____

____

Action Steps:

- Set rules for yourself for things that cause you to worry. Example: Checking email before bed caused me to worry about what had to do in the morning, so now I don't let myself check email in the evenings.
- Find activities that allow you to focus on something else (yoga, walking, exercise, reading, music, etc.). Commit to doing these daily to incorporate them into your life

NOTES

LESS DEBT MORE FREEDOM

Every once in a while I like to play a game with myself where I daydream about having no debt at all. I dream about how much money I would give away and what vacations I could go on. I dream about the space I would have to do what I want. Debt is an obligation and one that can be stifling if we le it get out of control. Debt can also be a healthy thing to leverage if you know how to. I would bet that most of us would gladly have less debt than we have today. If you find yourself relating to that last sentence, take some time this month to dream a little. Don't stop there. Let's turn these dream into reality as well!

- *"Too many people spend money they haven't earned, to buy things they don't want, to impress people they don't like." ~ Will Smith*
- *"The quickest way to double your money is to fold it in half and put it in your back pocket."*
- *"Know what you own, and know why you own it." - Peter Lynch*

Inventory:
List out all your outstanding debt as of today:

____

____

____

____

____

____

____

At your current rate of paying off debt, when will your loans be paid off?

____

What are things you have paid for in the past month that are "extras" or luxuries?

____

____

____

____

____

____

Action Steps:

- If you haven't mapped out what you spend each month on all major categories, go do sc (utilities, housing, cars, insurance, groceries, clothing, fun, etc.). Spreadsheets work really well to map this out month by month.
- Find a way to carve $25 dollars out of your normal spending this month.
- Research if it makes sense to consolidate any of your loans or refinance.

NOTES

LESS EXHAUSTION MORE ENERGY

Sometimes we would do well to pay attention to what our body is telling us. We can feel physically exhausted, as well as emotionally and mentally exhausted too. Sometimes life throws us curve balls and we go through seasons of more exhaustion than others. It's okay to feel tired, but when we do, we need to consider if we should be taking better care of ourselves. Rest is a wonderful thing and one that can do wonders if we let it.

- *"Do not confuse my bad days as a sign of weakness. Those are the days I am actually fighting my hardest." - Anonymous*
- *"Self-compassion is simply giving the same kindness to ourselves that we would give to others." – Christopher Germer*
- *"Almost everything will work again if you unplug it for a few minutes, including you." – Anne Lamott*

Inventory:

Do I feel rested in the morning?

____

____

How many true "breaks" do I take each day?

____

____

Are there any times of the week where people can't reach you?

____

____

What are some activities you enjoy doing that you find relaxing?

____

____

Action Steps:

- Read before bed each night for two weeks.
- Incorporate yoga and stretching into your daily schedule.
- Write out a nighttime routine you can test out.
- Schedule restful and relaxing things to do each week for the next month.

NOTES

LESS CHEMICALS MORE HEALTH

In 2015, the Huffington Post shared an article that said the average woman puts 515 chemicals ON her body. When I think through the countless articles I see about the stuff they make 'food' with, I can't help but wonder how many chemicals we put IN our body. I don't think I need a big FDA stud to tell me that simplifying my diet and home routine would make my life healthier. As I've done baby steps to simplify these two routines of my home life, I find it makes life simpler, PLUS healthier.

- *"The best six doctors anywhere and no one can deny it are sunshine, water, rest, air, exercise and diet." ~Wayne Fields*
- *"There is no one giant step that does it. It's a lot of little steps." -Unknown*
- *"Health is a state of body. Wellness is a state of being." ~J. Stanford*
- *"The food you eat can either be the safest & most powerful form of medicine...or the slowest form of poison." ~Ann Wigmore*

Inventory:

What are 2-3 products in your home (eating or cleaning routines) that you know need to go or change?

____
____
____
____

How many of my cleaning products do I need to lock up around little kids or puppies?

____
____
____

What steps have I already made in having less chemicals that I can celebrate already?

____
____
____

Action Steps:

- Make one swap this week for a healthier alternative. What's it going to be?
- Research 2-3 more things you're going to do to swap for healthier alternatives.
- Make a Pinterest board of healthy recipes and healthy cleaning tips so that you have a "go-to" spot when you want to continue this process.
- Evaluate your morning routine with the Think Dirty app or other 3rd party evaluation tools to see how healthy the products you use are.

NOTES

LESS COMPARISON MORE JOY

Comparison is a sneaky little thing that finds a crack and grabs hold. Comparison steals us from our own joy and continues to direct our attention on what other people are doing. All the while, we lose focus on our own strengths and own goals. Have you met someone who doesn't compare themselves with others ever? I've never met someone like this. So, instead, I ask you to join me on a journey this month to have less comparison in our lives. This is a journey we will be on throughout our entire lives, but it's one worth starting.

- *"Comparison is the thief of joy." - Theodore Roosevelt*
- *"Happiness is found when you stop comparing yourself to other people." - Anonymous*
- *"Don't compare your life to others. There's no comparison between the sun and the moon. They shine when it's their time." - Anonymous*
- *"The reason we struggle with insecurity is because we compare our behind-the-scenes with everyone else's highlight reel." -Steve Furtick*

Inventory:

Write out the things you tell yourself you aren't good at:

____
____
____
____
____
____
____

Who do you compare yourself to most regularly?

____
____
____

How often do you catch yourself comparing yourself to others? What is the scenario or situation where this happens most?

____
____
____
____
____
____

Action Steps:

- Take a break from social media.
- List out your accomplishments and successes.
- Verbally tell yourself each day, three strengths and things you are good at.
- Make a running list of something each day of the month that you are grateful for.

NOTES

LESS WASTE MORE BEAUTY

Leave no trace is a phrase I first learned when I started going hiking. This simply means that you leave nature looking the way you found it. Even though it makes perfect sense as you're hiking through the most scenic spots in the country, I think it has application on a daily basis. What kind of footprint am I leaving by the decisions I make each day? How much waste am I producing? Do I need to be producing it? How am I making my world more beautiful than I found it? Challenging myself to produce less waste is not about judging my habits as much as it is about encouraging better stewardship and beauty in the world.

- *"The Earth is what we all have in common." - Wendell Berry*
- *"Never doubt that a small group of thoughtful, committed citizens can change the world; indeed it is the only thing that ever has." - Margaret Mead*
- *"Nature is painting for us, day after day, pictures of infinite beauty." —John Ruskin*
- *"You cannot get through a single day without having an impact on the world around you. What you do makes a difference and you have to decide what kind of a difference you want to make." Jane Goodall*

Inventory:

How big is your trash can? How about your recycling? How full is each one each week?

____

____

____

When was the last time you looked at the packaging of the products you buy? How much of the wrapping do you toss out?

____

____

____

What do you buy that is quality and lasts vs. is a "good deal" and doesn't last long?

____

____

____

What ways can I make my nearby environment more beautiful?

____

____

____

Action Steps:

- Find three things you have thrown out this week and brainstorm ways you can reuse them.
- Find three things you tossed out this week that you didn't need to buy in the first place.
- List one thing you could do this month to decrease your trash and waste.
- List one long term habit you could form to decrease your waste.
- "Use it up, wear it out, make it do, or do without."

NOTES

LESS HURRY/BUSY MORE MARGIN

We all have the same 86,400 seconds in a day, but sometimes it feels like that's still not enough. I find myself hurrying from thing to thing, meeting to meeting, social event to social event. While these can be all good things, the hurry is not. Anyone else eat lunch in their car recently? Anyone have days where you barely have time to pee? Yea, I'm raising my hands for all of those. But, what if there was a better way? What if there was a way to have more margin and room to breathe in the day? What if instead of rushing from one thing to the other, I instead was able to see the hurts and needs of those around me? What if I saw the opportunities? What if I had space to dream and be creative? And, WHAT IF, by doing so, I was able to open up space for others to do the same?

- *"God made time, but man made haste." ~Irish Proverb*
- *"Nature does not hurry, yet everything is accomplished." ~Lao Tzu*
- *"Once you stop rushing through life, you will be amazed how much more life you have time for." ~Author Unknown*
- *"Remember the great adversity of art or anything else is a hurried life." ~Robert James Waller*

Inventory:

Do I tend to arrive on time, early, or late to most events or meetings?

____

____

If I had 30 extra minutes a day to do whatever I wanted with, what would I do?

____

____

____

____

How much "free" time do I have in a typical week?

____

____

____

What needs to go in terms of your schedule?

____

____

____

Action Steps:

- Schedule in extra buffer in between all of your appointments in the upcoming weeks.
- Set an alarm to go off during one of your breaks to remind you to look around at those around you.
- Doodle and daydream each day for a week about what you want your life to look like in the future.
- Time yourself on how long it actually takes for you to get out the door.

NOTES

LESS JUDGMENT MORE LOVE

It's a slippery slope from comparison to judgment and sadly, it's one that we fall into far too often. The world needs more love, not hate. Is it possible for us to put aside our opinions of others and their actions and simply love them? Is it possible to put aside our desire to be "right?" Is it possible to have friends who are different than us? Judging others is a tricky thing because we may think others do this and we surely don't. I wonder if we'll say the same thing at the end of the month.

- *"When you judge others, you do not define them, you define yourself." - Earl Nightingale*
- *"If you judge people, you have no time to love them." - Mother Teresa*
- *"Most people need love and acceptance a lot more than they need advice." - Bob Goff*
- *"(...) we're all rough drafts of the people we're still becoming." - Bob Goff*
- *"Be curious, not judgmental." – Walt Whitman*

Inventory:

What does it feel like when I've been judged or felt disapproving judgment from someone else?

____

____

When was the last time I placed direct or internal judgment on someone?

____

____

How many friends do I have that have differing beliefs in religion, politics, race, or other hot topics?

____

____

If people were asked about me, would they say I am a judgmental person?

____

____

Action Steps:

- Verbalize what the other person's reasoning might be for their position or choices.
- Do something loving for people who you disagree with or have judged (whether they knew about your perspective or not)
- Ask for forgiveness from anyone you who is on your conscience.
- Catch yourself when you are judging others and instead wish a blessing upon that person.
- Make a habit of giving people compliments regularly. The more you focus on the positive, the less time you have to judge.

NOTES

LESS ADULTING MORE FU

I don't know about you, but I need reminders not to take myself so seriously. When I can find oppo tunities to have fun and insert a little whimsy into daily life, I need to take them. I need to find way to laugh more, smile more, and have more fun. I need these simple reminders because I can easily get sucked into the many things to do in a day and the practical needs. Perhaps you can relate as well.

- *"My philosophy is: If you can't have fun, there's no sense in doing it."* - Paul Walker
- *"We didn't realize we were making memories, we just knew we were having fun."* - Anonymous
- *"Never underestimate the importance of having fun."* - Randy Pausch
- *"Having fun is the best way to learn."* - Albert Einstein
- *"People rarely succeed unless they have fun in what they are doing."* - Dale Carnegie

Inventory:

When was the last time I laughed so hard I cried?

____

____

What activities do I find enjoyable?

____

____

What are things I do that have no monetary or practical benefit, but are purely for fun?

____

____

How much fun do I have in a given week?

____

____

Action Steps:

- Carve out one activity in the next two weeks that is purely for fun.
- Watch a YouTube video by a comedian you like. Watch a few videos if you want to get really crazy.
- Force yourself to smile for ten seconds each day. See if you find yourself smiling naturall afterwards.

NOTES

LESS DISTRACTION MORE PRESENC

When was the last time you were truly present with those around you? Or, were you distracted by the latest notification on your smart phone? Time is precious and the people in our lives are too. Our world is full of distractions, pinging us from every angle...if we let it! Let's take a hard look at how present we are with people this month and how we can fight for this quality time.

- *"There are only two days in the year that nothing can be done. One is called yesterday and the other is called tomorrow, so today is the right day to love, believe, do and mostly live." - Dalai Lama*
- *"The art of life is to live in the present moment." - Emmet Fox*
- *"The real gift of gratitude is that the more grateful you are, the more present you become." - Robert Holden*
- *"Forever is composed of nows." – Emily Dickinson*

Inventory:

How much time do I spend on my smart phone? Check your phone settings to see! Am I shocked by this number at all?

____

____

Who do I want to connect with more?

____

____

____

____

How often do I check my phone, tablet, smart watch, or computer when I am at a meal or with family?

____

____

____

Action Steps:

- Make a goal to decrease your screen time b 20% this next week.
- Write out any "rules" you are setting for yourself. For example, "I will keep my phor in the bedroom during meals."
- Turn off unnecessary notifications on your phone or computer.

NOTES

Printed in Great Britain
by Amazon